Hamilton Duck's Springtime Story

Story and pictures
by Arthur Getz

MERRIGOLD PRESS • NEW YORK

Early one morning,
Hamilton Duck woke up.

He heard a bird singing and singing.

"Spring is here!
Spring is here!
Spring is here!"
sang the bird.

"I shall go for a walk
and enjoy the springtime," said Duck.

Hamilton Duck saw
his shadow in the sunshine.

He smelled the spring flowers
and picked a bunch.

Then he watched while
Mr. and Mrs. Barnswallow
came home from the South.

Duck took a long swim in the duckpond.
A mother duck was teaching her babies
how to swim.

Friendly Fish and
Hamilton Duck rubbed noses.
"Hi," said Friendly Fish.

After the swim, Duck decided to take
a little nap in the shade.

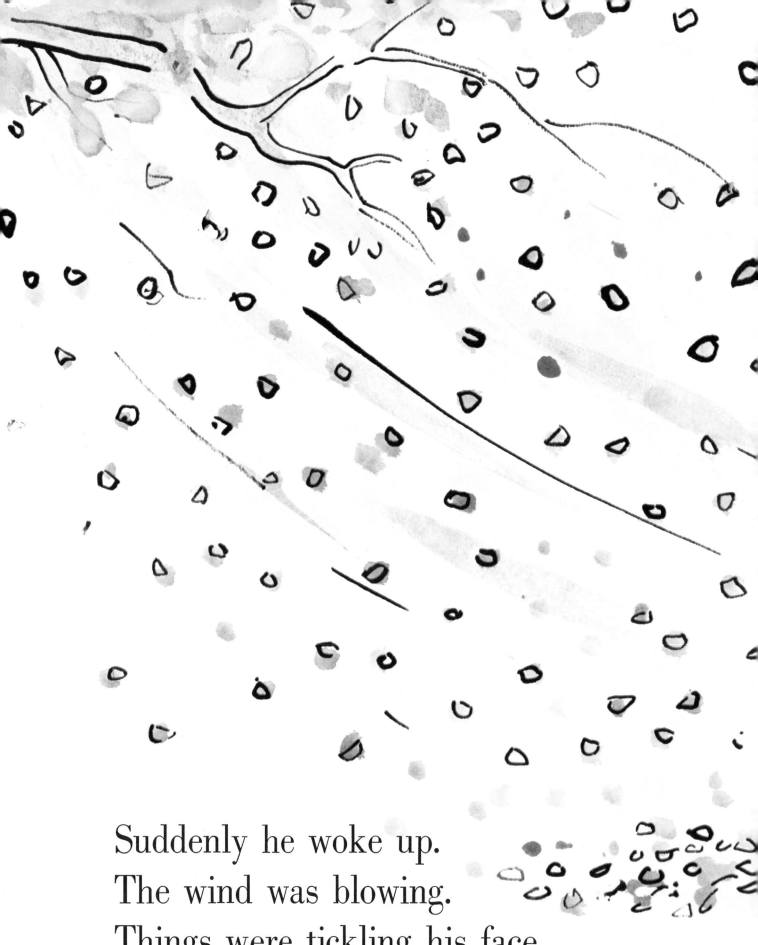

Suddenly he woke up.
The wind was blowing.
Things were tickling his face.

"It's snowing!" said Duck.
"Winter has come back.
I'm in the middle of a
snowstorm!"

"I'll get chilly.
I'll catch a cold."

"How nice
this snow smells,"
thought Duck.

"And it is pink.
I'm in the middle
of a pink snowstorm
which has a nice smell!"

Suddenly Hamilton Duck stopped.
"Why, this is not snow," he said.
"These things are blossoms. I fell
asleep under the apple tree."

He went back and picked up
his bunch of flowers.

It wasn't winter after all.

Spring had really come.